THIS BOOK BELONGS TO:

Illustrations & design by Jonas Claesson
Words by James Redmayne
Thanks to Stephanie Blank for countless hours of help, all your support
and always being honest when I ask - what do you think about this
drawing...

First Edition
Printed in Canada
ISBN 978-1-944242-83-1

Special thanks to all my Instagram friends and Kickstarter backers,
without you this book would not have been made - thank you!

This book, T-Shirts, Art Prints and more are available on my website.
www.jonasclaesson.com
shop.jonasclaesson.com
instagram.com/jonas_draws

# THE
# SURFING
# ANIMALS
## ALPHABET

ILLUSTRATIONS BY JONAS CLAESSON

WORDS BY JAMES REDMAYNE

I am a surfer, I surf every day.
I meet many people
along the way.

But I recently saw something
strange as can be,
A procession of animals
out in the sea!

The first was an Anteater,
with a snuffly long nose.

Aa
Anteater

Then came a Badger,
hanging all of her toes.

Bb
Badger

Third was a Cheetah,
spotty and quick,
Standing up tall
right under the lip.

Cc
Cheetah

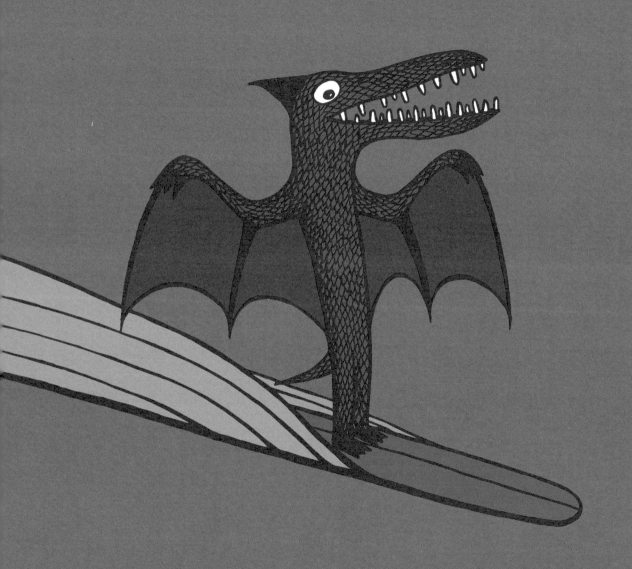

We haven't seen Dinosaurs
for a long time,
'Til this one turned up
flying down the line.

Dd
Dinosaur

Just one wave makes each surf
worthwhile,
Like this backhand barrel
in Elephant style!

Ee
Elephant

Flamingoes are graceful,
leggy and lithe,
Perfect for pulling
a quick cheater five.

Ff
Flamingo

Gravity doesn't seem to apply,
When this big Gorilla
takes to the sky.

He tells his mates, but they
always just laugh.
That's why he hired
the photog' Giraffe!

Gg

Gorilla

This Hippo is shy
in the heat of the day,
But during a night surf
she comes out to play.

Hh
Hippo

Iguanas are possibly
coolest of all,
With this over-head,
hand-plane,
tail-drag stall.

# Ii
Iguana

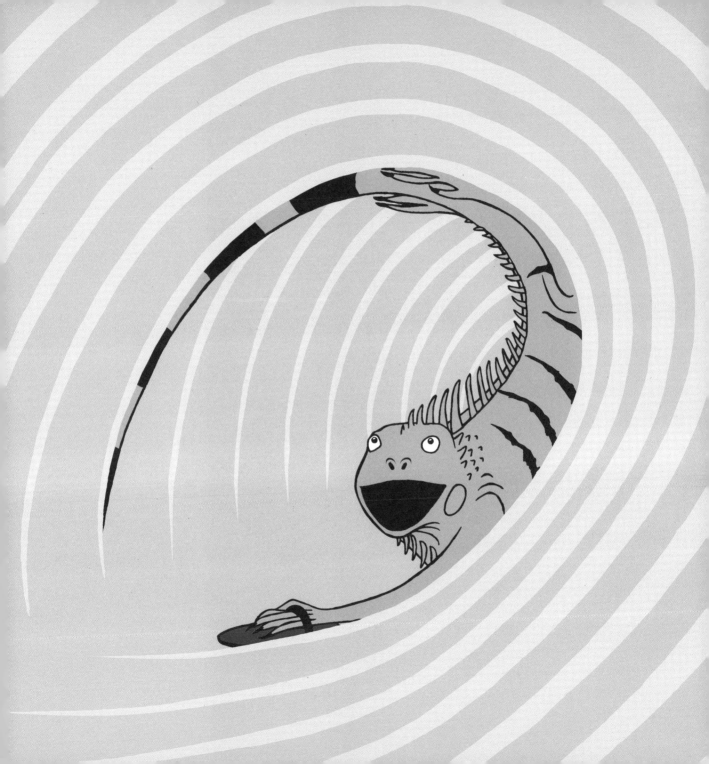

Log-riding's all about
style and grace.
Watch this spotty Jaguar
glide down the face.

Surfing tandem is tricky to do,
Unless you have a pouch
like this Kangaroo!

Kk
Kangaroo

A big air reverse
is a difficult trick,
Unless you're a Lemur
who's little and quick.

Ll
Lemur

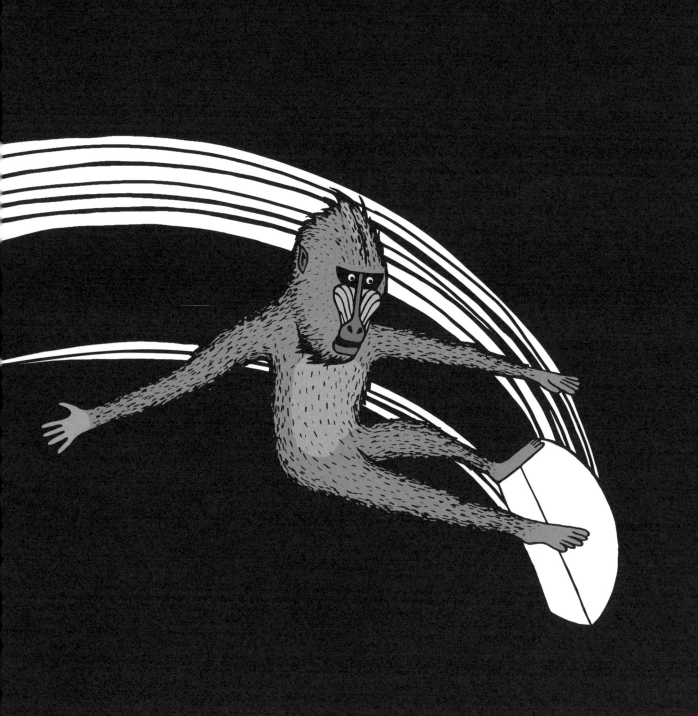

This Mandrill turns
in a powerful way,
Using his rail
to send buckets of spray.

Mm
Mandrill

The Narwhal is a classy chap,
With pointed tusk
and a feathered cap.
Here he is, just leaning in,
To keep his board
in perfect trim.

Nn
Narwhal

This Orangutan shows you a
very good tip:
A good bottom turn
helps you get to the lip.

Orangutan

Little Penguin knows there is
fun to be had,
On a day at the beach
for a surf with her Dad.

Pp
Penguin

This spotted Quoll,
an Australian creature,
Is surfing her way
to a magazine feature!

Qq
Quoll

As his colourful quad
sails through the air,
The Raccoon grabs his rail
for extra flair.

Rr
Raccoon

Sloths are so lazy they spend
all day in bed,
Except when it's offshore
and the swell's overhead!

S s
Sloth

Riding a barrel's the
ultimate aim,
And this tube riding Tiger's on
top of his game!

To stall for a barrel
he sets his rail,
Then burns off some speed
with his paw and his tail.

Tiger

It's hard to go in
when conditions are right,
So the Unicorn surfs on,
right into the night.

Uu
Unicorn

The Vulture studied her
weather charts well,
And swoops right on in
to catch the new swell.

Vv
Vulture

When you first try to surf
you might find it quite tough,
Your board seems to wobble,
the waves seem so rough!

With practice and practice
you'll learn how to stand,
Like the sure-footed Wombat
with a drink in his hand!

Ww

Wombat

The Xenopus is
a type of frog,
Who usually surfs
on an old school log.

But when she's keen
for some big-wave fun,
She'll surf with her step-up,
a lightning-bolt gun.

Xx
Xenopus

Yaks live on mountains
far far away,
But this one has come
for a beach holiday!

Yy

Yak

Last was the Zebra,
striped white and striped black,
In perfect position,
about to get shacked!

Zz
Zebra

And that is all of our surf-
boarding friends,
As our animal alphabet
comes to an end.

But the next time you go to
the beach - look around!
'Cos you never quite know
what there is to be found.

THE
# SURFING
# ANIMALS
ALPHABET

Fan of the surfing animals?

Check out my other work with animals gone camping, vanimals,
surf trip adventures and more.
Shop.jonasclaesson.com - for prints, clothing and other fun stuff
Instagram.com/jonas_draws - for all my latest drawings
or say hi! hello@jonasclaesson.com